CONTENTS

THE MOORLAND BALANCE

The Science Behind Grouse Shooting and Moorland Management

Game & Wildlife
CONSERVATION TRUST

First published in Great Britain in 2017 by
Game & Wildlife Conservation Trading Ltd
Burgate Manor, Fordingbridge SP6 1EF
www.gwct.org.uk

A catalogue record for this book is available from the
British Library.

First printed July 2017

ISBN: 978 1 901369 27 4

Designed and typeset in Minion Pro by
James Swyer and Louise Shervington

Front cover © Tom Hartley
Inside front cover © David Mason.

Foreword

In the eyes of country sports followers, driven grouse shooting is the supreme challenge, the most blissful joy. To its foes, however, it represents all manner of things they recoil from: they believe that they see simply rich men in antique fancy dress killing wild creatures for their amusement, in a setting that should properly be the playground of raptors and hillwalkers. The GWCT seeks to use scientific research to demonstrate that what urban visitors perceive as wildernesses in a state of grace are, in truth, landscapes that demand expensive management for the benefit of all wildlife.

Today, moor owners and shooters pay the bills for this. If the opponents of grouse shooting ever get their way and the sport is banned, no one has produced a credible explanation of how Britain's heather hills can continue to be cherished, without imposing a heavy new burden on the public purse, on both sides of the northern border. The old libertarian arguments in support of country sports- that they should be accepted as part of the warp and woof of rural life, which urban dwellers have no right to interfere with - no longer suffice. Only science, hard evidence about the positive contribution of shooting to the environment in general and the uplands in particular, can make it possible to sustain grouse shooting in the face of increasingly fierce opposition. Only the Game & Wildlife Conservation Trust (GWCT) has provided this in years past, and can continue to do so in the future. All of us who love the sport owe a debt to the Trust for the fact that we are free to shoot grouse today. All of us who wish to continue to do so in the future should recognise how vital is the need to support its work, to make the case for the place of the grouse harvest in 21st century British country life.

Sir Max Hastings

Preface

This guide has been prepared to clarify just how much is, and is not, known about the sustainable management of our uplands. The Game & Wildlife Conservation Trust (GWCT), a research and education charity conducting this essential conservation science, is well placed to help inform this debate.

For over 80 years we have been researching and developing game and wildlife management techniques and have had 135 scientific papers published in peer-reviewed journals on issues relating to upland ecology over the past 46 years.

On the basis of our scientific expertise and credibility, we regularly provide advice to such statutory bodies as Defra, Scottish Natural Heritage and Natural England. We also provide practical advice to farmers and landowners on how to manage their land with a view to improving biodiversity.

Much of our research is undertaken in collaboration with other institutions and organisations, including the following: Exeter, Imperial College London, Newcastle and Aberdeen Universities, the British Trust for Ornithology, the Centre for Ecology and Hydrology and the RSPB.

To help disseminate this knowledge, representatives of the GWCT sat on over 100 external committees in 2015, including the following: Defra's Upland Stakeholder Forum, Natural England's main board and the UK Birds of Conservation Concern Panel.

Grouse Shooting

What are grouse and where are they found?

There are four species of grouse in Britain: the red grouse, the black grouse, the ptarmigan and the capercaillie. Capercaillie are a protected species with fewer than 2,000[5] individuals in a few pine-dominated Scottish woodlands. Like the capercaillie, ptarmigan are also only found in Scotland, but only above 800m altitude and are notoriously hard to count. The black grouse population is UK-wide and estimated to be 5,100 males[5]. They are found on moorland and woodland edges, either coniferous or birch.

Red grouse are one of our few endemic sub-species, meaning that they are only found in the UK. The population is estimated to be

230,000 pairs[5]. They are found on heather moorland including both areas of blanket bog and upland shrub heath. All grouse populations fluctuate in size over the years so these figures are a mid-point estimate.

Which grouse are shot on driven grouse moors?

Red grouse. They are regarded internationally as the paragon of gamebirds; their attraction has not been superseded by the ubiquitous pheasant. The marketplace confirms this view; the cost of driven grouse shooting can be five times that of a pheasant day for a similar number of birds shot.

So red grouse are wild birds?

Yes. Grouse moors are entirely dependent on wild birds, unlike many pheasant or partridge shoots, which rely on rearing and releasing. This is because reared red grouse survive badly when released, and grouse moors have maintained many parts of our upland ecosystem in a suitable condition for wild birds. This differs from large parts of the lowlands, which have been heavily affected by modern development and agriculture, and can no longer support a big population of wild gamebirds.

Is driven grouse shooting the one where shooters wait for the birds to come to them?

Yes. Red grouse, pheasants and partridges are 'driven', where birds are flushed by a line of beaters and fly over the people shooting, who are stationary in a line. On grouse moors they typically stand in a line of 'butts' – screened stands for one shooter. But red grouse are also shot 'walked-up', where the participants walk across the moorland, flushing birds as they go; and 'over dogs', where walking shooters use trained pointing dogs to find grouse.

Are there benefits of driven grouse shooting over walked-up shooting?

Yes. Driven moors invest more in staff, time and equipment, which allows more consistent predator and disease control and enhanced habitat management. A driven grouse shoot can make this additional private investment because the private and market demand for driven shooting is higher, and therefore so is the economic return[6]. Walked-up shooting is a highly engaging sport, but it cannot typically provide the wide range of associated benefits provided by driven shooting because of its lower economic turnover.

What are the conservation benefits of driven shooting?

Moors managed for red grouse are shown to be better than other land uses in maintaining heather-dominated habitat[1], and both directly and indirectly support the species that depend on or thrive in it. This is important because 75% of the world's heather moorland is found in Britain[7]. In addition, many species of upland birds, including curlew, lapwing and golden plover, are more numerous and breed more successfully on moorland managed for red grouse than on other moorland not managed in this way[2,3,8,9]. The way the keepers manage the land is beneficial to these birds, some of which are of conservation concern, and whose populations are declining nationally and internationally[10].

Are these benefits widely recognised?

Yes. In response to the last petition to ban driven grouse shooting, the UK government released a statement recognising that *"When carried out in accordance with the law, grouse shooting for sport is a legitimate activity and in addition to its significant economic contribution, providing jobs and investment in some of our most remote areas, it can offer important benefits for wildlife and habitat conservation"*[11].

Conservation on grouse moors

What are the primary reasons the GWCT supports grouse moor management?

There are three main reasons:
1. The habitat management undertaken on grouse moors preserves and enhances heather-dominated habitats[1].
2. The package of management, notably habitat enhancement along with predator control, contributes to the conservation of a suite of upland bird species including upland waders[2–4]. Preservation of habitat and wildlife thus stems a national loss to land-use change, predation pressure, climate change and wildfire[1].
3. This is a land use that delivers high nature conservation value but is funded primarily by private investment and supports local communities economically, socially and culturally.

Why is heather moorland so important?

Heather-dominated moorland habitat supports many biological communities that are either only found in the UK, or are better developed here than elsewhere[12]. 13 of these communities are listed under EC Directive 92/43/EEC on the Conservation of Natural Habitats and of Wild Flora and Fauna. This environment also supports a unique collection of bird species (an "assemblage"), which contains 18 species of European or international importance[13]. The 1992 Rio Convention on Biodiversity ratified the global importance of UK heather moorland[14].

Okay, but don't other countries have heather too?

Yes, but none have extensive heather uplands. Most other heather areas are lowland or coastal, leaving the UK responsible for 75% of the world's heather moorland[7]. Until the early 2000s heather cover was falling sharply in the UK, generally as a result of overgrazing and/or commercial forestry plantations. Many of the best areas are in our national parks and are protected as Sites of Special Scientific Interest (SSSIs) or are 'Natura' sites – Special Areas of Conservation (SACs) and Special Protection Areas (SPAs) – in recognition of their importance. This is the highest level of EU habitat protection.

Which bird species thrive on moors managed by gamekeepers?

Many birds do better on moors managed for red grouse than on less-managed moorland. These include globally threatened species such as curlew and merlin but also red grouse, black grouse, golden plover, lapwing, snipe, greenshank, buzzard, short-eared owl and black-headed gull[2,8,9]. However, there is also evidence that other species including crow, meadow pipit and skylark do less well on grouse moors, in some cases because they prefer a grassier environment[2,3].

Isn't curlew our bird species of highest conservation concern?

Yes. Scientists from the RSPB published a paper in 2015 stating that the curlew should be considered our most pressing bird conservation priority. Several studies show curlew do better on grouse moors in terms of either abundance or breeding success. This is probably because of a combination of factors that benefit them, including predator control and heather burning[2–4,9,15].

The curlew is considered our species of highest conservation concern. © Laurie Campbell

What about merlin?

A recent study of merlin divided England into one kilometre squares and looked for evidence of breeding merlin. These squares were then correlated with a map of known grouse moors to see where merlin are breeding. 80% of squares containing merlin were found to be on grouse moors, with only 20% on non-grouse moors, so it is clear that grouse moor management helps provide a suitable nesting environment for these birds[16].

Heather-dominated heath landscapes are maintained by grazing and burning. © David Mason

Okay, but do we really need to manage moors for these species to thrive?

Without moorland management, these species would still exist, but at much lower densities, in less well-connected populations, leaving them at greater risk of local extinction. British moors are the product of thousands of years of management by man. Forests were cleared and vegetation maintained by grazing and burning to produce the heather-dominated heath landscapes that now exist. If management ceased, heather would be lost from all but the highest and wettest areas and replaced with scrub and tree regeneration. Some species would benefit and some would decline, notably those that prefer open landscapes.

What happens when driven grouse shooting stops?

Heather moorland would probably be converted to either grazed grassland or forestry;, meaning that the important heather habitat would be lost. It is known that management for driven grouse shooting slows the loss of heather from our landscape; a GWCT study showed that, between the 1940s and 1980s, moors that stopped grouse shooting lost 41% of their heather cover, while moors retaining shooting lost only 24%[1]. However, many areas currently under management for red grouse are now also designated as SSSIs or SPAs for wildlife. Although grouse moor management is acceptable on these sites, the environmental impact of forestry or heavy grazing means that these alternatives would not be permitted. Therefore, banning driven grouse shooting would likely lead to abandonment of these areas and the current management of heather and peatland would cease.

What happens to the wildlife when grouse moors are left unmanaged?

Grouse moor management was abandoned in the Berwyn Mountains in north Wales in the 1990s. As a result of management stopping, curlew, lapwing, golden plover, redshank, red grouse and black grouse populations have all declined to the point where several species are extinct in some areas[17]. Many of these are the very species that the area was designated to protect.

Species such as lapwing have declined in the Berwyn Mountains after grouse moor management was abandoned in the 1990s.© Dave Kjaer

Golden plover flourish on moors managed for grouse shooting. © Dave Kjaer

Heather burning

What is prescribed heather burning?

This practice has several names – rotational burning, muirburn and prescribed burning. It is the planned burning of small areas of older heather, with the aim of achieving a low intensity, quick, 'cool burn' in small patches, which removes the canopy but does not affect the underlying peat or soil layer.

Why is it done?

As heather and grass plants become older, they become less palatable (tasty) and less nutritious (tougher and lower in nutrients). The process of burning small areas removes the older growth and allows the plants to regenerate after the burn. New heather and grass shoots follow, and these, along with the flush of plants such as bilberry or blueberry, are key food for red grouse, deer, mountain hares and livestock. Burning patches of heather in different years in this way provides a patchwork of areas of heather of different heights. This mosaic provides areas that are suitable for feeding, breeding and cover in close proximity to each other, and is beneficial not only to grouse but also to other moorland birds[18].

When is heather burning carried out?

Various laws only allow burning to be carried out between October and April. Most burning occurs in the spring when the plant material has dried out, allowing it to burn while cold, damp conditions underfoot mean the fire is most easily controlled. Burns are not performed in summer when birds and animals are breeding, the daily temperatures are warm, fuel is variable in dryness, and underlying peat may have become dryer.

Are there heather burning guidelines or legislation that land managers must follow?

Yes. Defra and Natural England set out and manage the rules for safe burning and can fine or prosecute those who do not burn in line with them. Where there is an increased risk to other landscape features or species, a licence must be applied for in order to burn heather.

Is heather only burnt on grouse moors?

No. Although it is often associated with this land use, and presented as such in the media, heather burning is carried out for livestock grazing on moorland, as well as in other environments. A recent study of land use in Scotland looked at 26 estates and found that heather burning occurred on 23 of these, although grouse shooting was only the main land use on 10. The others stated their predominant management was for deer stalking, sheep grazing or conservation. Those estates that manage for grouse shooting had 15% of land managed by burning per year, compared with 5% of land on other estates[9].

So burning is good for animal food, but what effect does it have on moorland biodiversity?

A recent independent report by Natural England, '*The effects of managed burning on upland peatland biodiversity, carbon and water*', examined all the appropriate scientific literature related to burning, which we refer to heavily in answer to the following questions[19]. With respect to biodiversity, most studies examined in this report indicate an overall increase in species richness or diversity when burning is considered at a whole moor level[19]. Burning affects the invertebrate species (including insects, spiders and earthworms), lichens, mosses and higher plants present on moorlands, removing some and supporting others in the regenerating areas.

Because burning takes place in small areas typically leaving over 85% unburned in a year and 65% unburnt for more than three years, many studies assessing the whole of a moor indicate an overall increased biodiversity. A recent moorland review by Scottish Natural Heritage (SNH) noted that much of the conservation benefit from burning depends on local site management and conditions[20]. Furthermore, a recent article examining moorland sites in Scotland over 44 years concludes that without burning, biodiversity decreases and states *"to maintain diversity, timely burning is recommended"*[21].

Can burning also boost curlew numbers?

Yes. A recent paper shows that curlew are more abundant as the percentage of recently burnt ground increases[9]. Golden plover also prefer to nest in areas of heather, particularly where burning has occurred in the last five years. As with any land management intervention, heather burning influences the species that live in the area. Some species will benefit and some will be disadvantaged.

Do conservation organisations use it?

Yes. Fire is an important and widely used management tool with a vital role to play in the maintenance and recovery of several habitat types, including heather moorland. SNH and Natural England burn heather and gorse and approve its use on many moorland SSSIs; the RSPB burns on a number of its upland reserves; the national park authorities recognise the value of muirburn and use it on Exmoor and in the New Forest to improve grazing; the National Trust has burning regimes on many of its upland holdings; and the Wildlife Trusts set fires to burn brash in coppice woodland and reed swamp.

So species that thrive on grouse moors will be okay if other moorland users burn the heather?

No, because along with heather burning, grouse moor management also includes predator control, while few other upland habitat managers undertake this activity sufficiently to reduce predation on ground-nesting birds. See the section on *Upland Predator Control* for more information.

What would happen to the vegetation if the heather were not burnt?

It depends on the environment in question. All upland moors tend to be lumped together when discussing these complex issues, whereas in fact there are several distinct ecosystems, including blanket bog/deep peat, and heather-dominated dry heathland.

Okay, so what would happen on blanket bog/deep peat?

Areas that experience high rainfall and low temperatures, usually at high altitude, with ground that is waterlogged for most of the year, can produce areas of 'blanket bog', where a peat layer of variable depth covers the whole landscape. Heather in these areas may be naturally prevented from becoming rank by compression under deep winter snow cover, which allows side shoots to touch the ground, root and spread laterally. In such areas, the need for heather burning is lower as the heather grows more slowly.

What would happen on heather-dominated heaths?

The current landscape of open heathlands dominated by heather is generally perceived as a 'natural' environment, whereas in fact it is the product of thousands of years of management by man. Forests were cleared, and vegetation maintained by grazing and burning to produce the heather-dominated landscapes that now exist. If management in these areas were stopped, heather would become old and degenerate and ultimately be lost, bracken would spread, scrub and tree regeneration would gradually occur, and over many decades it would progress to a vegetation community of shrubs, bushes and trees.

Is there an alternative to heather burning?

Moorland habitats can be maintained in a mosaic of heights and densities by burning, grazing and more recently cutting. Grazing alone is difficult to manipulate between too little and too much, but can be an important management technique used alongside burning or cutting. Cutting requires low slope angles and smooth terrain to avoid machinery damage. Where access is possible it can be a valuable tool in areas of high fire risk or fire impact. Care needs to be taken not to cause compaction damage with machinery, or leave dense cut litter, which suppresses regrowth of the heather.

HEATHER BURNING AND PEAT FORMATION

In controlled muirburn only the growing plants are burnt, not the peat. © GWCT

How is peat formed?

Certain plant species tend to be thought of as peat-forming, including mosses and sedges. These grow and die back in waterlogged conditions. The low oxygen content of these conditions prevents rapid decomposition of dead material to humus (like compost). Instead, the plant remains are slowly compressed as more dead material falls each season, these layers of matter eventually turning into peat. The peat is deepest where wet conditions are maintained for thousands of years, shallowest where the climate is drier and ground conditions more free-draining.

Why burn peat?

Peat is not burnt. In controlled muirburn only the growing plants are burnt. Uncontrolled fires, maliciously or carelessly set, can burn into peat causing very severe damage and loss of carbon.

Does heather burning affect peat formation?

Research into the effect of burning on Sphagnum species gives mixed results. Some studies indicate that the rate of peat accumulation may be lower where managed burning is used[22], however recent evidence suggests that where the interval between prescribed burning is short (10 years), the abundance of Sphagnum increased. This remains true when comparing ground under 10-year burning rotation to ground that has not been burnt for 60 years[23]. The paper finds "no evidence to suggest that burning is deleterious to peat-forming species; indeed, it was found to favour them". The evidence is conflicting and further research is needed.

Can heather burning affect the underlying peat?

Sometimes, and sometimes not. The answer to this question depends on many factors, including what sort of burns are performed (i.e.. size, temperature), the frequency, and the type of peat that is present. The answer can range from there being no effect in the case of appropriately performed and controlled 'cool' heather burning, to there being a severe effect in the case of 'hot' burns and serious wildfire.

What do you mean by 'cool' and 'hot' burns?

'Cool' burns pass quickly over the surface, burning the over-ground vegetation but not affecting the humus or litter layer on the surface of the peat. The temperature at ground level remains low. 'Hot' burns occur when the fire passes more slowly, burns more intensely and incorporates lower layers of vegetation. This can result in ignition of the underlying peat, temperatures becoming higher still, and difficulty in controlling the fire.

Why is heather burning being used as a reason to ban or regulate driven grouse shooting?

Although heather burning is carried out in other settings, it is often associated with land managed for grouse. Particularly driven grouse shooting, as higher numbers of birds are needed to operate this kind of shooting. Where heather burning is not performed appropriately, negative effects can be seen.

What can these negative effects be?

Poorly performed or poorly controlled heather burning, or wildfires, can have a negative effect on the underlying peat; contribute to the release of greenhouse gases or carbon (of which peat is a major store); have a detrimental effect on water quality; and lead to wildfires.

HEATHER BURNING AND WATER QUALITY

Are studies on the impact of burning on water quality conclusive?

No. The effect of heather burning on water quality is still being studied, with different pieces of evidence suggesting different outcomes. There is some evidence that burning may be associated with increased water colour, and some sources equate this to an increase in dissolved organic carbon (DOC) in the water. However, one study clearly showed that the colour of water is not always a good indicator of DOC, and that DOC did not rise in response to burning[24]. One recent paper showed that lake water DOC fell following a wildfire. The picture is not yet clear.

Why is the impact of burning on water not yet fully understood?

Results differ depending on the length of time since burning, and the scale at which the studies are performed. The possible effect of burning on water quality and amount of run-off is also complicated by interactions with other upland management, such as woodland expansion and grazing. These interactions have been little studied.

How do I understand the true situation when the evidence is not clear cut?

This is a difficulty that is often encountered in the early stages of research into a complex subject. The evidence base is building up but has not yet revealed a definitive answer. There are many reasons for this, including the interplay of many factors and the complexity of the wide variety of ecosystems under consideration. Furthermore, management practices such as 'burning' in fact consist of a range of techniques with many variables. A simple answer to such questions is rarely available, and a balanced review of the facts often reveals a more complex picture.

Those that attempt to present a simplistic view do not represent all the evidence. This view was expressed in a recent peer-reviewed paper by 13 authors who are concerned about the simplistic and provocative position taken towards burning by many bodies. They state *"We, therefore, suspect that much of the contextualisation in recent fire-related studies stems less from evidence of the environmental effects of managed burning and more from attitudes towards the forms of land-ownership and other management practices associated with burning in the UK"*[25]. Until integrated evidence is available, all scientists should be concerned when potentially interesting and informative research is used as a forum to propagate what amounts to hearsay or to promote political agendas[25].

Without heather burning, would water from moorland be clear?

No. Water from peatlands has always been what the water industry calls 'discoloured', as a result of draining through the peat. It is likely that water draining through upland forestry would be similarly discoloured. Evidence suggests that heather burning can be associated with increased water colouration[19], but this is not conclusive. The EU has set standards for water quality that go beyond its purity and safety and include its colour. Water companies must therefore treat water from peatlands to meet these standards. Many water companies have land holdings in upland areas and rent their land for grouse shooting. This would be unlikely to happen if it was damaging water supply.

Is anything being done to address some of the possible effects of upland burning on water?

The moorland management community do not want to unintentionally cause water quality issues, or burn unnecessarily. Natural England has been working with moors on a transition process to enhance blanket bog and also sustain grouse shooting for the last four years. This 'outcomes approach' is site specific; for example, on some moors by re-wetting, on others by focussing burning away from blanket bog where the benefits to grouse of burning appear lowest, and the risk to Sphagnum greatest.

Moorland wildfires

What causes wildfires?

The evidence base examining the causes of vegetation fires is very limited. The Fire Service Incident Recording System does not include cause or source of ignition, unless an investigation is conducted which is very rare for vegetation fires. Therefore, the relationship between the use of prescribed fire and the frequency and extent of wildfires on moorland remains unclear. This is an area which needs more research.

Does prescribed heather burning lead to wildfires?

There is evidence that sometimes prescribed burns are not adequately controlled and can lead to wildfires[20]. However, evidence also suggests that the benefits for wildlife, wildfire reduction and promoting habitat growth outweigh the risks. For example, in the Peak District, grouse moor management is associated with a lower frequency of wildfire[26]. There is evidence across the world for the benefits of prescribed burning in reducing wildfire risk[27], but there are not enough studies specifically referring to the UK moorlands, and experts call for more research[25,28].

How can rotational burning reduce wildfire risk?

Fuel load and structure are critical factors in how fire behaves. Prescribed burning reduces the accumulation of old, woody heather, which can build up to a large stock of potential fuel, so heather burning reduces the likelihood (and intensity) of fire[19]. Prescribed burning may also create fire breaks, which can hinder the spread of wildfire.

Are wildfires always bad?

Wildfires are uncontrolled and may burn hot and deep, in the worst cases igniting the underlying peat and burning for months. This can then also lead to a cost to the public purse with extensive and prolonged use of the fire and emergency rescue services in difficult to reach areas. These factors are very rare occurrences in prescribed burns. However, there is also evidence that wildfire can have little or no lasting impact on habitat or wildlife[20].

Burning creates new heather and grass shoots that are key food for red grouse and other wildlife.

Moorland drainage

Why were our moors drained?

Although some moorland drainage is centuries old, in the 1960s and 70s government subsidies were paid to moorland owners to dig drainage ditches (sometimes called 'grips'). Drainage was performed with the purpose of lowering the water table and removing surface water to improve the vegetation for livestock grazing, as part of the post-war drive for "more food from our own resources". At the time there were thought to be benefits to grouse as well in improved food, cover and reduced disease transmission.

What else did successive governments encourage drainage for?

Large areas of British moorland have been drained for commercial forestry[29], and woodland planting on the hill and hill edge continues to affect our hydrology. More than half of the agricultural land in Britain has been drained[29].

Did the GWCT advise moor owners to dig drains for grouse?

No. As far back as 1970 our advice was that draining on level waterlogged peat was slow, costly, usually ineffective, and could lead to gully erosion[30].

What are the effects of drainage?

Upland drainage has been associated with several negative effects on moorland, including changes in water flow over and through the soil, with increases and decreases in flood peaks, lowered water table, altered sediment flow, erosion, increased colouration of water and reduced invertebrate populations. For these reasons, many upland landowners, including grouse moor owners, are actively blocking drains to restore moorland at their own expense. The Moorland Association has reported an estimate by Natural England that around 18,000 hectares of moorland habitat on grouse moors has been restored across northern England[31].

How are moors being 'rewetted'?

Various methods are being used on a site-by-site basis. Typically, drains are physically blocked at intervals. Drains can be blocked with peat if they are small and on a flat area. Larger drains have been blocked with bales made of woody stems of heather, wood or plastic dams. Innovative drain-blocking uses old fishing nets filled with crushed glass. Some drains can also be 'reprofiled' where steep edges are flattened out, reducing flow rates and encouraging plant growth.

Will this solve downstream flooding?

No, because eventually all these peatlands will be full of water with no more capacity. The National Ecosystem Assessment indicated that the opportunities for peatland restoration to modify runoff regimes were likely to be slight and were uncertain, but should be taken[32]. In the long run, however, fully rewetted systems will not contribute to slow water release as saturated peat is 98% water and the water table so high that there would still be the likelihood of rapid runoff response.

Does heather burning on grouse moors increase flooding?

Although there are relatively few studies available, the authors of a recent Natural England report could not find any evidence for burning increasing flood risk, and state that: "No evidence was identified specifically relating to the effect of burning on watercourse flow or the risk of downstream flood events. If there are any effects, these are likely to be highly site specific."[19] A recent study examining the effect of rotational burning on deep blanket peat sites drew several conclusions. These include that the lag time to peak runoff is increased on burnt sites for most rain conditions – meaning that the movement of water is slowed down across areas managed with burning – and that, for the heaviest 20% of storms, the lag time is the same but that the peak flow is higher from burnt compared to unburnt catchments[33]. Once more, the evidence base regarding a possible impact of prescribed burning on flood risk is not conclusive.

Sheep tick management is important for the welfare of grouse and other moorland birds. © GWCT

Disease control on grouse moors

What veterinary interventions are used on grouse moors?

Diseases are controlled in livestock (most often sheep) and in red grouse on moors. In both animals the parasites controlled are internal worms and external blood-sucking ticks. Though the two species share the same tick species, the internal worms they have are different.

Why are ticks a problem?

The sheep or deer tick (*Ixodes ricinus*) found on sheep also feed on red grouse and other moorland birds, to whom they can pass a virus called the louping-ill virus (LIV). LIV disease can cause up to 80% mortality in red grouse chicks.

What is done about this?

The number of ticks that are present in a given area can be reduced by limiting the number of hosts – a very long-term approach – or treating the hosts. Sheep have been treated with anti-tick medication (acaricides) for over 50 years for their own health. To reduce the number of ticks on moorland, generally the sheep need to be dipped once or twice more than usual in the summer.

The GWCT have developed and continue to research new methods of tick control. If a large population of deer are providing an additional host and inflating the tick population, deer numbers can be reduced on the moor.

Are these treatments dangerous?

No. The medication that is used to reduce ticks on sheep that graze moors is the same as that used on sheep farms across the country.

Do these ticks also affect humans?

Yes. Ticks also bite humans, and our dogs, where they can be a vector for the *Borrelia* parasite that causes Lyme disease. This can be very serious if not diagnosed and treated.

What about other moorland birds?

Ticks also feed on other moorland birds. Although it appears that waders such as curlew do not contract LIV, excessive tick burden has been cited as a cause of mortality for curlew chicks[34]. It is known that high numbers of ticks attached around the face can be debilitating for the chicks of moorland birds. In one study 91% of curlew broods contained chicks carrying ticks at an average of 4.5 ticks per chick, and a maximum of 64 ticks on one individual[35].

What else is administered to the animals on grouse moors?

Upland sheep and red grouse suffer from different parasitic worm infections, though the chemicals used to treat them are the same. Sheep are regularly treated throughout the year against a range of gut parasites to prevent loss of condition and poor lambing. In red grouse the most important disease (strongylosis) is caused by the strongyle worm and has a similar effect, reducing survival and breeding performance.

Historically, strongylosis has driven grouse population cycles, with crashes in red grouse numbers as a result of this disease every few years. If strongylosis is affecting the birds on a moor, medicated grit can be provided under the supervision of a veterinarian. This controls the parasite, improving the survival and breeding performance of the grouse population.

Are all moors distributing this medicated grit all the time?

No. Use is regulated and it is only provided when the birds need it, when prescribed by a vet. Typically demonstrating need involves the moor collecting sample worm burden data from grouse to test for worm numbers.

What effects could the grit be having on the environment or other species?

The active ingredient that is applied to the grit is called flubendazole, which is an anti-nematode (worming) agent that is given to livestock across the country in far greater quantities than would ever be present on a moor. As a licensed medication, it has passed thorough investigations into the effect on non-target species, as well as the wider environment.

Curlew numbers rose by 14% per year after legal predator control was implemented. © Dave Kjaer

Upland predator control

Why is predator control necessary?

The modern world has created an environment where generalist predators thrive to the extent that they can seriously impact on the status of a wide range of vulnerable species, especially ground-nesting birds, such as red and black grouse, lapwing and curlew. For example, a large European study has shown that 65% of curlew nests observed between 1996 and 2006 were destroyed by predation[36].

Why is it acceptable to control one animal for the benefit of another?

The justification for predator control as part of game management is that it leads to good conservation of wildlife and habitats in the countryside, as long as it does not threaten the conservation status of our native predators. Many of the prey species are of conservation concern, whereas many of the predators in question are thriving.

Do predators really have such a large impact on prey populations?

In some circumstances, yes. Since the early 1980s, the GWCT has published over 150 papers considering predation effects. These clearly show that predation pressure can depress numbers of game and other wildlife[37,38]. The reduction in abundance is caused by losses of adults, eggs or young. Reviews of many research papers indicate that predator control can support the recovery of declining species of wildlife[39].

Does reducing predators actually help those vulnerable species?

Yes, where predator control is done to an effective level, and habitat is suitable. Many of the benefits of grouse moor management, particularly for the grouse and breeding waders, and species such as mountain hares, come directly from legal predator control. For the bird species this has been shown by an experimental study examining the effect of predator control alone. Predator control allowed ground-nesting birds to breed on average three times more effectively than when predators were not controlled[4].

Did this improved breeding success lead to larger populations?

The effect of this on the curlew population was marked – in the absence of predator control, curlew numbers were dropping by 17% per year. When legal predator control was implemented, curlew numbers rose by 14% per year (after a lag period as the new chicks reached breeding age)[4].

We have calculated that the low breeding success seen on moors where predators were not controlled in this experiment could lead to a drop in lapwing and golden plover numbers of 81%, and curlew of 47%, after 10 years[40].

What do you mean by 'legal predator control'?

Lethal control of certain abundant generalist predator species is allowed under UK law, without individual licences. The methods used are regulated by the legislation, and are also guided by best practice codes.

© GWCT

Is predator control only done on grouse moors?

No. Grouse moor keepers are not alone in controlling predators; many conservation bodies control them for the protection of vulnerable wildlife. Foxes and crows are controlled by and for many farmers to protect lambs and breeding ewes. Predator control is an essential part of supporting rare species such as the grey partridge in lowland areas, and mink are routinely killed in order to protect water voles on Wildlife Trust reserves.

What predators are controlled?

The main species targeted are foxes and carrion crows but also stoats, weasels, rats and feral cats.

How are they controlled?

Spring trap, cage trap, snare or shooting. All are regulated activities in the UK, with training advisable in all regions and mandatory in some parts of the UK. Best practice is continuously researched and revised by the GWCT.

What effect does it have on predator numbers? Will they go extinct?

In regions where a high game interest predominates, for example where several neighbouring properties are managed principally for grouse, some predators could be scarce as a result. Low numbers in one area can be offset by good numbers of the same predators in other regions, so that the conservation status of the predators is secure, while other important ecosystem services are being delivered as a consequence.

HEN HARRIERS AND RED GROUSE

Is there a conflict between driven grouse shooting and the conservation of birds of prey?

Yes. Our research shows that the predation on grouse by a large number of hen harriers and other raptors can prevent a grouse population recovering from a low density.

Has this actually happened?

Yes. The Joint Raptor Study (1992-1996) and subsequent studies at Langholm Moor in Scotland described how a grouse moor could become uneconomic because of raptor predation and no longer support moorland management. Here the gamekeepers lost their jobs, there were knock-on effects in the local economy, and numbers of ground-nesting birds declined, including waders and hen harriers themselves. Without new kinds of management such as diversionary feeding and brood management, you cannot have viable grouse shooting alongside large numbers of hen harriers.

How many hen harriers are there in the UK?

As hen harriers are a migratory species, it depends when in the year you count them. In terms of nesting birds, in 2010 there were 630 hen harrier nests in the UK[5,41]. A national survey has been undertaken in 2016 and we await these results.

How many hen harriers are there in England?

Hen harriers don't stay within the borders of countries so again it depends when you count them. England has higher numbers of harriers during migration and in the winter, when harriers visit from Scotland and continental Europe. Counts are not made of how many stay all year in England.

How many breed in England?

The most recent published scientific paper reporting breeding hen harriers across the UK was in 2010 and found 12 nests[41]. Natural England also monitors the number of successful nests reported each year, and this number fluctuates – in 2013 there were no successful nests, and in 2015 there were six[42].

How many hen harriers could settle in England and not affect land management?

The Environment Council harrier mediation process modelled how many harriers could settle and have only a minimal effect on land management[43]. Based on an estimate of the area of suitable habitat, a sustainable number could be 82 pairs of hen harriers in England.

You say 'suitable habitat' – how much of that is on grouse moors in England?

50% of the suitable English habitat is found on grouse moors – so there could be up to 41 pairs on English grouse moors.

© Laurie Campbell

Why are there so few hen harriers on the 50% of suitable habitat in England that has no driven grouse shooting?

It is likely to be a combination of harrier nests being predated, lack of food[44], disturbance, and possibly failing to have enough birds settled in an area to make it attractive to others. Two papers, published in 2013 and 2016 identified that hen harriers benefited from the control of predators, such as foxes and crows, performed by gamekeepers to protect red grouse[45,46]. Another paper published in 2014 noted that over half the hen harrier breeding attempts on Skye failed due to predation[47]. More research is needed.

Why are there so few hen harriers on English driven grouse moors?

In addition to the reasons above, it has been shown that illegal culling by gamekeepers can restrict hen harrier numbers on some grouse moors[48,49]. If there are too many harriers on a moor the shoot becomes uneconomic, the gamekeepers lose their jobs, and numbers of ground-nesting birds decline, including ones of conservation concern such as waders. The Joint Raptor Study and subsequent studies at Langholm demonstrated that this situation can really happen and is no exaggeration.

So what can be done?

Now, after 15 years of talks, 20 reports, three governments and six years of mediated conflict resolution talks, the aim is to implement the Defra Hen Harrier Action Plan, published in January 2016. This plan recognises the source of the conflict, and brings together several approaches to mitigate it. The combination of diversionary feeding, brood management, winter and roost protection, reintroduction into previously occupied areas, population monitoring, and increased intelligence and prosecution efforts offers the best solution to resolve this divisive issue.

Mountain hares and red grouse

Where are mountain hares found?

Mountain hares are native to Britain, and used to live across the country, but the introduction of the brown hare in Roman times led to the retreat of mountain hares to the uplands. Mountain hares can feed on heather and other moorland plants, while the brown hares need lowland grasses and agricultural crops. Now, there is a large core population in the Scottish Highlands, a well-established population in the Southern Uplands, and a small one in the Peak District. Those in northern Wales have probably died out in the last two decades.

How many mountain hares are there in Britain?

The last figures, published in 1995, suggested that there were approximately 350,000 mountain hares in Scotland, but this is just an estimate. We don't know how many there are in absolute terms because hares are hard to count; they are well-camouflaged with 'crouch and freeze' behaviour. We do know something about their range and how many are killed each year, which act as indexes of change. The best way of counting hares to get a density figure is the subject of ongoing research undertaken jointly by the GWCT and the James Hutton Institute in Scotland.

What information do we have?

Currently most of the information on hare population trends is drawn from reports to the GWCT about the number of hares shot on estates as part of the GWCT's National Gamebag Census (NGC), and two surveys for government that mapped the hare's range.

Is the population of mountain hares declining?

Since the 1950s, when keepering increased again after World War II, the NGC shows a clear cyclical pattern of peaks and troughs. This very long-term data shows that changes in numbers of hares by more than tenfold are quite natural. Despite these large short- and medium-term changes, there is no discernible long-term trend in numbers of hares in the bag.

So hare populations naturally fluctuate?

Yes. Research suggests that hare numbers can fluctuate naturally for many reasons: parasites, weather, predation and habitat quality. Natural declines of '5-100 fold' followed by recovery are a feature of bag records long before culls for disease control were an issue. This suggests that large bags indicate high hare abundance rather than high cull rates, and vice versa. However, research is needed to better understand how trends in bags are influenced by changes in cull effort.

If populations change so much, how would we know if the mountain hare population were genuinely declining?

Range contraction is often the first sign of a population in trouble. This means that the area in which the species lives is shrinking. The GWCT established in 2008 that the Scottish range of mountain hares is not shrinking[50]. In fact, Scottish mountain hare densities have regularly been 10 times higher than are typical in continental Europe.

Do mountain hares live on grouse moors?

Yes. Heather moorland actively managed for red grouse provides very good habitat for mountain hares. It is probably the intensive fox control, combined with rotational burning to produce young heather growth, that benefits both grouse and hares[50].

Are mountain hares culled on shooting estates?

Although mountain hares thrive on grouse moors, hares can sustain high levels of ticks and the tick-borne louping-ill virus, bringing them into apparent conflict with red grouse. However, we have always been clear that the priority for disease control should be treating sheep and deer management before considering hare culls. Where these measures have been implemented and ticks remain a problem for grouse, hare numbers may need to be temporarily reduced to suppress the parasite and disease.

Is that legal? Aren't mountain hares protected?

It is legal, as long as it is done sustainably. The mountain hare is listed under Annex V of the EU Habitats Directive (1992) as a species "of community interest whose taking in the wild and exploitation may be subject to management measures". As well, Article 14 of the directive requires member states to ensure that the exploitation of such species "is compatible with their being maintained at a favourable conservation status".

Does the population persist after a cull on a grouse moor?

Yes. Hares are commonly seen even in areas where there are intensive culls, suggesting that the population is more robust than commonly portrayed. However, this cannot be taken for granted, and sustainable management of hares must go hand in hand with sustainable management of grouse. Improved monitoring methods would help us understand the effects of culls, with the NGC as a means of putting current hare bags in the context of past changes in bags. This is a sound, evidence-based perspective for policy makers.

Would hares benefit from banning driven grouse shooting?

It would depend on what land use replaced grouse shooting. However, the Mammal Society says the following[50]:

> *"Mountain hare numbers have declined locally where favourable habitat such as former grouse moors has been afforested or heather has been removed by excessive grazing. Young forestry plantations can support high densities of hares which sometimes cause significant damage to trees, but these high densities decline once the forest canopy closes, and the ground vegetation is diminished."*

Our research would also suggest that without predator control and the maintenance of open moorland, mountain hare numbers would fall, and likely become fragmented, increasing their risk of local extinction. It appears grouse moor management has driven our uniquely high densities of mountain hares, so grouse moor managers should be encouraged to take responsibility for maintaining this situation.

ALTERNATIVE MOORLAND USE

Why do our moors need to be 'used'?

Moorlands would not exist without being 'used', i.e. having an economic purpose; they are cultural landscapes extending back thousands of years. In the uplands, grouse and deer shooting, livestock grazing and forestry can provide an economic return while also supporting a uniquely important landscape, range of habitats, and wildlife. Our lowlands have been much more affected by land use than our uplands.

What else can these moors be used for?

Many of the areas where moorland is used for grouse shooting are classified as Less Favoured Areas (LFAs), indicating that agricultural production or activity is more difficult because of natural handicaps. The historical options for profitable use of the land are few, being mainly limited to grazing by livestock, commercial forestry or game management. Tourism benefits from the maintenance of these open upland landscapes but rarely makes a contribution to the maintenance costs. Commercial or state incentives would be needed to drive other upland land uses such as carbon storage, renewables or water management.

Which land use is 'better'?

All land usage has an impact on the environment. Specific consequences of these land uses have been identified but it is our belief that a direct comparison of "which is better?" is not possible or appropriate. Different species thrive in different environments, therefore sustainable biodiversity on our moorlands is best supported with a varied mix of management across the wider landscape[9].

A similar position is true for other ecosystem services such as carbon storage, flood protection, cultural value or economic activity. The UK National Ecosystem Assessment report did not attempt to describe better or worse ecosystems for this reason, noting that: "For mountains, moorlands and heathlands to continue providing high levels of ecosystem service flows long into the future, the management of these habitats must be sufficiently flexible to allow adaptation to a range of currently uncertain future conditions."[32]

Alternative moorland use: Forestry

How much commercial forestry is there in the UK?

Commercial forestry blocks consist of fast-growing, non-native tree species. Many of these have been planted in the UK in the second half of the 20th century, often in response to government initiatives. One reference states that around 20% of UK moorland is now afforested with coniferous plantations[28].

What effect does forestry have on the moorland environment?

The most obvious effect is that of habitat replacement. The community of species that thrive on heather moorland is not the same as that which inhabits commercial forestry. When these forestry blocks mature, they become dense, dark, and relatively biodiversity poor.

So are the moorland bird communities affected?

Yes. As an example, 15 years after afforestation of the Southern Cheviots, the forest canopy closed, and as a result all the upland bird species disappeared. The losses for that area were estimated to be 1,750 pairs of curlew, 1,200 pairs of golden plover, 200 pairs of dunlin, 25 pairs of merlin, and all the red grouse, snipe, redshank, wheatears, ring ouzels and hen harriers[52].

Are there other effects?

Yes. Prior to planting, drainage ditches are often dug and fertiliser may be applied, which affects the nutrient composition of the soil. The drains lower the water table, with resulting compression and shrinkage of peat as it dries out, a process that accelerates once the tree canopy closes. Large-scale cracking of the peat can result[28].

Are these effects limited to the area containing the trees?

No. Drying and shrinkage can occur some distance away from the forestry block itself. Bird communities in the surrounding moorland can be affected up to a kilometre from the forest edge, with reductions in golden plover and dunlin, and reduced curlew breeding success[28].

Why are these effects on moorland birds seen so far from the trees?

Research indicates that it is likely to be due to increased predation, with more predators living in the forestry block, or taking advantage of it to provide cover when hunting[3].

Are there effects on water quality and flow?

Yes. Streams that drain afforested areas tend to be more acidic. Water flow is also affected, with both total flow and stream peak flow increasing following drainage, and reducing once the block matures (after perhaps 20 years)[28].

Are there effects on carbon cycles?

Yes. Although carbon is taken up as the forest matures, there may be severe depletion of the soil carbon store through increased decomposition of the soil. Some research shows that there can be a net release of carbon dioxide into the atmosphere, although the overall effects on greenhouse gases are not yet clear[28].

ALTERNATIVE MOORLAND USE: FARMING

How important is farming in the uplands?

The UK National Ecosystem Assessment says that livestock farming over many generations has contributed to the cultural and environmental heritage of today's countryside, and many things our society values beyond food may depend on upland farming in the future. Probably 15% of the UK land area is upland farming[32].

How does livestock grazing affect moorland?

Comprehensive reports from Natural England and Scottish Natural

© GWCT

Heritage examine this area in great detail. Light, seasonal grazing is good for sheep, heather and consequently grouse. However, it is generally accepted that large increases in the number of sheep during the second half of the 20th century led to overgrazing, and that this grazing pressure had detrimental effects on moorland. Stocking densities have generally reduced recently, and this can improve heather cover and condition, but there is as yet little evidence for large-scale improvements in habitat in response to this[53].

What sort of detrimental effects can overgrazing have?

The most well-established effect is the reduced condition or extent of heather cover, and replacement with grass-dominated vegetation[28,53]. This carries with it effects on the species that are associated with the heather habitats described earlier. However, other species, for example skylark and meadow pipit, may benefit from a change from heather to grassland. Once more, a balance of habitats is likely to provide the highest biodiversity.

Are there any other effects?

There may also be effects on the ecosystem services such as water and carbon (discussed for other forms of moorland management). Once again, these are difficult to establish with certainty. Studies conclude that there can be a link between grazing and soil erosion and loss, but that the effect on carbon capture and storage is variable and there is little effect on water quality[53]. However, another review from 2007 suggests that grazing may affect water flow across moorland so much that stopping grazing may reduce flood risk[28].

Does all grazing cause these problems?

No. A light, preferably mixed regime of grazing seems to provide benefits in terms of environmental services and biodiversity, however this may not be compatible with profitable livestock farming[52]. Unfortunately, a sheep density low enough to prevent damage to the habitat is generally below the level at which it is economically viable. The measures that are required to improve profitability, such as drainage and liming, can be damaging to the heather moorland and its ecosystem.

Can there be a balance?

Grouse moors need sheep grazing to provide habitat management, and in some places to help control tick numbers. Sheep graziers need moorlands to summer graze their flock, preserving their improved grass for winter forage and grazing, and benefit from low numbers of foxes and crows. Management arrangements between grouse moors and sheep graziers provide for an incentive to manage heather moorland sustainably, maximising outcomes such as high nature value and rural employment, while minimising habitat damage.

COMMONLY HEARD CRITICISMS OF DRIVEN GROUSE SHOOTING

Claim	Comment
Conservation organisations want to ban it	The RSPB does not support a ban on grouse shooting. The National Trust has no wish to see grouse shooting banned and rents large parts of its upland holdings for driven grouse shooting.
There is illegal persecution of raptors by grouse moor keepers	Such persecution is illegal and the perpetrators should be prosecuted. The fact that some people break the law is not justification for destroying the livelihoods and way of life of their innocent colleagues.
This rich man's hobby damages the environment and society	Rarely does a hobby contribute so extensively to jobs, wildlife protection and internationally important habitats. There are, of course, trade-offs for which evidence is increasing and thus practical solutions are becoming clearer. Banning such a hobby would be akin to banning forestry because there are downsides for brown hares. Instead we recognise the good that comes from woodland and work to integrate it into our landscape.

Claim	Comment
Heather burning contributes to the release of greenhouse gases because it releases carbon dioxide	There is evidence that managed burning (along with many other things) can affect the carbon cycle, but national reviews have concluded, with respect to overall carbon budgets, that: "So far, research has produced inconsistent evidence, with predictions including both positive and negative effects of burning."[18]
Heather burning on grouse moors increases flooding	Although there are relatively few studies available, the authors of a recent Natural England report could not find any evidence for burning increasing flood risk, and state that: "No evidence was identified specifically relating to the effect of burning on watercourse flow or the risk of downstream flood events. If there are any effects, these are likely to be highly site specific."[18]

References

1 Robertson PA, Park K, Barton A. Loss of heather moorland in the Scottish uplands: the role of red grouse management. *Wildlife Biol* 2001; **7**: 37–42.

2 Tharme AP, Green RE, Baines D, Bainbridge IP, O'Brien M. The effect of management for red grouse shooting on the population density of breeding birds on heather-dominated moorland. *J Appl Ecol* 2001; **38**: 439–457.

3 Douglas DJT, Bellamy PE, Stephen LS, Pearce-Higgins JW, Wilson JD, Grant MC. Upland land use predicts population decline in a globally near-threatened wader. *J Appl Ecol* 2014; **51**: 194–203.

4 Fletcher K, Aebischer NJ, Baines D, Foster R, Hoodless AN. Changes in breeding success and abundance of ground-nesting moorland birds in relation to the experimental deployment of legal predator control. *J Appl Ecol* 2010; **47**: 263–272.

5 Musgrove A, Aebischer N, Eaton M, Hearn R, Newson S, Noble D et al. Population estimates of birds in Great Britain and the United Kingdom. *Br Birds* 2013; **106**: 64–100.

6 Sotherton N, Tapper S, Smith A. Hen harriers and red grouse: Economic aspects of red grouse shooting and the implications for moorland conservation. *J Appl Ecol* 2009; **46**: 955–960.

7 Tallis J, Meade R, Hulme P. Blanket Mire Degradation. In: Tallis J, Meade R, Hulme P (eds). *British Ecological Society*. Manchester, 1998, pp 1–2.

8 Baines D, Redpath S, Richardson M, Thirgood S. The direct and indirect effects of predation by Hen Harriers *Circus cyaneus* on trends in breeding birds on a Scottish grouse moor. *Ibis (Lond 1859)* 2008; **150**: 27–36.

9 Newey S, Mustin K, Bryce R, Fielding D, Redpath S. Impact of Management on Avian Communities in the Scottish Highlands. *PLoS One* 2016; **11**.

10   Eaton M, Aebischer N, Brown A, Hearn R, Lock L, Musgrove A et al. Birds of Conservation Concern 4: the population status of birds in the UK, Channel Islands and Isle on Man. *Br Birds* 2015; **108**: 708–746.

11   UK Government D. Ban driven grouse shooting: Government response. 2016.https://petition.parliament.uk/petitions/104441?reveal_response=yes#response-threshold.

12   Thompson DB, MacDonald AJ, Marsden JH, Galbraith C. Upland heather moorland in Great Britain: A review of international importance, vegetation change and some objectives for nature conservation. *Biol Conserv* 1995; **71**: 163–178.

13   Sim IMW, Gregory RD, Hancock MH, Brown AF. Recent changes in the abundance of British upland breeding birds. *Bird Study* 2005; **52**: 261–275.

14   United Nations Environment Programme. Rio Declaration on Environment and Development. United Nations Conf. Environ. Dev. 1992.http://www.unep.org/documents.multilingual/default.asp?documentid=78&articleid=1163.

15   Thompson DBA, Gillings SD, Galbraith CA, Redpath SM, Drewitt J. *The contribution of game management to biodiversity: a review of the importance of grouse moors for upland birds.* Scottish National Heritage: Edinburgh, 1997.

16   Rogers S. Merlin Study Report. Report to the Moorland Association. Penny Anderson Associates, Buxton, 2014.

17   Warren P, Baines D. Changes in the abundance and distribution of upland breeding birds in the Berwyn Special Protection Area, North Wales 1983-2002. *Birds in Wales* 2014; **11**: 32–42.

18   Buchanan GM, Grant MC, Sanderson RA, Pearce-Higgins JW. The contribution of invertebrate taxa to moorland bird diets and the potential implications of land-use management. Ibis (Lond. 1859). 2006; **148**: 615–628.

19   Glaves D, Morecroft M, Fitzgibbon C, Owen M, Phillips S, Leppitt P. Natural England Review of Upland Evidence 2012 - The effects of managed burning on upland peatland biodiversity, carbon and water. Natural England Evidence Review, Number 004, 2013.

20   Werritty A, Pakeman R, Shedden C, Smith A, Wilson J. A Review of Sustainable Moorland Management. Report to the Scientific Advisory Committee of Scottish Natural Heritage. 2015.

21   Welch D. The floristic changes of Scottish moorland dominated by heather (*Calluna vulgaris*, Ericaceae) but unburnt for 50 years and kept checked by moderate grazing. *New J Bot* 2016; **6**: 31–42.

22   Garnett MH, Ineson P, Stevenson AC. Effects of burning and grazing on carbon sequestration in a Pennine blanket bog, UK. *The Holocene* 2000; **10**: 729–736.

23   Lee H, Alday JG, Rose RJ, O'Reilly J, Marrs RH. Long-term effects of rotational prescribed burning and low-intensity sheep grazing on blanket-bog plant communities. *J Appl Ecol* 2013; **50**: 625–635.

24   Clay GD, Worrall F, Aebischer NJ. Does prescribed burning on peat soils influence DOC concentrations in soil and runoff waters? Results from a 10year chronosequence. *J Hydrol* 2012; **448–449**: 139–148.

25   Davies GM, Kettridge N, Stoof CR, Gray A, Ascoli D, Fernandes PM et al. The role of fire in UK peatland and moorland management: the need for informed, unbiased debate. *Philos Trans R Soc London B Biol Sci* 2016; **371**.

26   McMorrow J, Lindley S, Aylen J., Cavan G, Albertson K, Boys D. Moorland wildfire risk, visitors and climate change: patterns, prevention and policy. In: Bonn A, Allott K, Hubacek K, Stewart J (eds). *Drivers of Change in Upland Environments*. Routledge: Abingdon, 2009, pp 404–431.

27   Boer M, Sadler R, Wittkuhn R, McCaw L. Long-term impacts of prescribed burning on regional extent and incidence of wildfires— evidence from 50 years of active fire management in SW Australian forests. *For Ecol* 2009.

28   Holden J, Shotbolt L, Bonn A, Burt TP, Chapman PJ, Dougill AJ et al. Environmental change in moorland landscapes. *Earth-Science Rev* 2007; **82**: 75–100.

29   Holden J. Artificial drainage of peatlands: hydrological and hydrochemical process and wetland restoration. *Prog Phys Geog* 2004; **28**: 95–123.

30   Watson A, Miller GR. Grouse Management. The Game Conservancy Green Guide, Booklet 12. Fordingbridge, 1976.

31   The Moorland Association. Highs and lows for start of grouse season. 2016.http://www.moorlandassociation.org/2016/08/highs-lows-start-grouse-season/.

32   UK National Ecosystem Assessment (2011). The UK National Ecosystem Assessment Technical Report. Cambridge, 2011.

33   Holden J, Palmer SM, Johnston K, Wearing C, Irvine B, Brown LE. Impact of prescribed burning on blanket peat hydrology. *Water Resour Res* 2015; **51**: 6472–6484.

34   Grant MC, Orsman C, Easton J, Lodge C, Smith M, Thompson G et al. Breeding success and causes of breeding failure of curlew Numenius arquata in Northern Ireland. *J Appl Ecol* 1999; **36**: 59–74.

35   Newborn D, Fletcher K, Beeston R, Baines D. Occurrence of sheep ticks on moorlandwader chicks. *Bird Study* 2009; **56**: 401–404.

36   Roodbergen M, van der Werf B, Hotker H. Revealing the contributions of reproduction and survival to the Europe-wide decline in meadow birds: Review and meta-analysis. *J. Ornithol.* 2012; **153**: 53–74.

37   Aebischer N. Gamebird science, agricultural policy and biodiversity conservation in lowland areas of the UK. In: Dickson B, Hutton J, Adams WM (eds). *Recreational Hunting, Conservation and Rural Livelihoods - Science and Practice.* Blackwell Publishing Ltd: Oxford, 2009, pp 197–211.

38   Sotherton N, May R, Ewald J, Fletcher K, Newborn D. Managing uplands for game and sporting interests. An industry perspective. In: Bonn A, Allott T, Hubacek K, Stewart J (eds). *Drivers of Environmental Change in Uplands.* Routledge: Abingdon, 2009, pp 241–260.

39   Smith RK, Pullin AS, Stewart GB, Sutherland WJ. Effectiveness of Predator Removal for Enhancing Bird Populations. *Conserv Biol* 2010; **24**: 820–829.

40   Aebischer N, Baines D, Ewald J, Jones C, Fletcher K, Foster R et al. Waders on the Fringe. Game and Wildlife Conservation Trust, 2010.

41   Hayhow DB, Eaton M a., Bladwell S, Etheridge B, Ewing SR, Ruddock M et al. The status of the Hen Harrier, *Circus cyaneus*, in the UK and Isle of Man in 2010. *Bird Study* 2013; **60**: 446–458.

42   Natural England. Hen harrier breeding season set to be most successful for 5 years. 2015.https://www.gov.uk/government/news/hen-harrier-breeding-season-set-to-be-most-successful-for-5-years.

43   Elston DA, Spezia L, Baines D, Redpath SM. Working with stakeholders to reduce conflict - modelling the impact of varying hen harrier *Circus cyaneus* densities on red grouse *Lagopus lagopus* populations. *J Appl Ecol* 2014; **51**: 1236–1245.

44   Amar A, Redpath S, Thirgood S. Evidence for food limitation in the declining hen harrier population on the Orkney Islands, Scotland. *Biol Conserv* 2003; **111**: 377–384.

45   Baines D, Richardson M. Hen harriers on a Scottish grouse moor: Multiple factors predict breeding density and productivity. *J Appl Ecol* 2013; **50**: 1397–1405.

46   Ludwig S, Roos S, Bubb D, Baines D. Long-term trends in abundance and breeding success of red grouse and hen harriers in relation to changing management of a Scottish grouse moor. *Wildlife Biol*; **In press**.

47   McMillan R. Hen Harriers on Skye, 2000–12: nest failures and predation. *Scottish Birds* 2014.

48   Potts G. Global dispersion of nesting hen harriers *Circus cyaneus*; implications for grouse moors in the UK. *Ibis (Lond 1859)* 1998.

49   Redpath S, Amar A, Smith A. People and nature in conflict: can we reconcile hen harrier conservation and game management. In: Baxter J, Galbraith C. (eds). *Species Management: Challenges and Solution for the 21st Century*. Edinburgh, 2010, p Chapter 18.

50   Patton V, Ewald J, Smith A, Newey S. Distribution of mountain hares Lepus timidus in Scotland: results from a questionnaire. *Mammal* 2010.

51   Mammal Society. Mountain Hares - *lepus timidus*. http://www.mammal.org.uk/species-hub/full-species-hub/full-species-hub-list/species-mountain-hare/.

52   Ratcliffe D. *Bird Life of Mountain and Upland*. Cambridge University Press: The Edinburgh Building, Cambridge, 1990.

53   Martin D, Fraser M, Pakeman R, Moffatt A. Natural England Review of Upland Evidence 2012 - Impact of moorland grazing and stocking rates. 2013.

Supporting the GWCT

The proceeds from this book will support the research, advice and education undertaken by the Game & Wildlife Conservation Trust.

The Game & Wildlife Conservation Trust is the leading wildlife conservation charity which provides scientific research into Britain's game & wildlife, research that has spanned over 80 years. Our work leads to improvements in habitat provision & wildlife conservation, coupled with developing sympathetic ways of managing the countryside for the benefit of Britain's wildlife. The Trust advises farmers, landowners & other environment organisations and wildlife charities on improving wildlife habitats & practices. The Trust lobbies for agricultural and conservation policies based on science & is actively consulted on & involved with leading organisations including Natural England, FWAG, Defra, Natural England, the Wildlife Trusts & many others.

The Trust uses science to promote game and wildlife management as an essential part of nature conservation and develop scientifically researched game and wildlife management techniques and support best practice for field sports that contribute to improving the biodiversity of the countryside.

You can join the Game & Wildlife Conservation Trust by calling 01425 652381 or visiting www.gwct.org.uk/join.